ALLANSON HICK

Architect and Artist
1898 – 1975

Compiled by
Arthur G. Credland

Hull City Museums & Art Galleries
and the Hutton Press

1991

Published by Hull City Museums & Art Galleries

and the Hutton Press Ltd.
130 Canada Drive, Cherry Burton, Beverley
North Humberside HU17 7SB

Phototypeset and printed by
Image Colourprint Ltd.
Anlaby, Hull

ISBN 1 872167 20 9

CONTENTS

Acknowledgements 4

Foreword 5

Introduction 7

Biographical Sketch 13

Paintings and Drawings in the Permanent Collection:

    (i)   Town Docks Museum 21

    (ii) Ferens Art Gallery 41

Pictures loaned for exhibition 45

Appendix 1: Pictures displayed at the Royal Academy........................ 55

Appendix 2: Subjects for calendars; exhibited 1976 58

ACKNOWLEDGEMENTS

The compiler of this publication is particularly indebted to the help and keen interest of Alan Bray and 'Sandy' Chamberlain and also to Dr. Margaret Sands for her enthusiasm in this project, as well as Mr. J. Robin Lidster, Mr. I. P. L. Rogerson, Miss Susan and Miss Jean Ferens.

I also wish to thank my colleague Ann Bukantas for assistance with material from the Ferens Art Gallery and Graham Edwards for photographing items from the museum collection. Ms. Allison Duffield of the Imperial War Museum and the staff of the Royal Naval Museum provided information on warships of the 1939-45 War and Barbara O'Connor, registrar of the National Maritime Museum, arrranged for the loan of works in the collections at Greenwich.

A. G. Credland,
Town Docks Museum,
Hull.
1991

FOREWORD

The City Council would like us to express thanks to the Hull Maritime Society whose generous contribution made it possible to acquire the valuable record made by Allanson Hick of activities in the Hull Docks during the 1939-45 War. The Society's regular meetings have done much to foster interest in the Town Docks Museum and the maritime heritage and associations of the City whilst the subscriptions of its members have contributed to several projects and acquisitions which have extended the scope of our maritime collections. New members are always welcome at the meetings now held in the Old Grammar School, or further information can be obtained from the Town Docks Museum.

We are also grateful to Arthur Credland, Keeper of Maritime History at the Town Docks Museum, who has carried out the research and made the contacts which have enabled the subjects of the archive to be identified. His work and the biographical sketch by Alan Bray, whose own watercolours have continued the Allanson Hick tradition of depicting the building of our city, have produced a permanent memoire of a fiery personality who did so much to retain the record and the appearance of Hull and its port during troubled years.

We are anxious that the City Museums and Art Galleries should play an important role in preserving both the present and the past of the city and its people. The acquisition of these drawings, and the publication of a detailed catalogue to accompany the exhibition, with the help of our collaborators, the Hutton Press, will surely bring a period of local history vividly back to those who remember the war years and give new insight to present and future generations.

Councillor T. P. Larsen JP,
Chairman of Culture Services Committee

John Bradshaw MA,
Curator of Museums & Art Galleries

June 1991

Allanson Hick (left) with H. H. Rodmell (right) at an exhibition in the 1950s.

ALLANSON HICK FRIBA RSMA SGA – Architect and Artist

INTRODUCTION

The idea of staging an exhibition devoted to the work of Allanson Hick had been in the air for a number of years but the acquisition of a large collection of drawings in 1990 was the immediate stimulus for the display which this booklet accompanies. More than seventy items were purchased for the Town Docks Museum with the aid of generous funding from the Hull Maritime Society. These sketches and watercolours were mostly executed during the 1939-45 War or within a few years after.[1] Hick had applied for a position as an official war artist and though this privilege was denied to him, he did gain permission to make drawings anywhere within the Humber defences. He clearly took full advantage of this opportunity and the artist has left us a unique record of the repair and refitting of warships in the Hull docks during the war, an activity not documented in any other way. Cameras were strictly forbidden but Hick was able to reproduce the ships externals including armaments and any outward signs of the top secret radar and direction-finding equipment within. Most bear the marks of the censor's pencil and stamps on the reverse either forbidding their publication at the time or making it conditional on the deletion of sensitive details such as ship serial numbers, radio aerials and any indication of location. On one occasion at least, in November 1944, the artist was able to hitch a ride on a destroyer while it was undergoing trials after a major refit, and he has given us a series of rapid sketches made above and below decks.

In several instances he records the precise day the drawing was executed and the time spent, twenty minutes for the rough sketch of the *Quest*, thirty minuted for the *Bedouin* but a total of four hours spread over two days for 'the wounded *Onslow*'.

Most if not all of these studies remained unpublished until the cessation of hostilities but in 1946 '*Onslaught's*

new shaft' formed the subject of his diploma piece for the Society of Marine Artists. A pen and wash version was shown at the Royal Academy in 1948 and this or another variant was hung at the RSMA exhibition so late as 1972.

The museum already possessed an 'on the spot' sketch, and drawing developed from it, of troops disembarking from *Empire Rapier* in 1947 which were given by the artist's nephew Alexander 'Sandy' Chamberlain; in addition he gave the Ferens a watercolour and two pencil drawings.[2] Already in the Ferens collection was a portrait in oils of E. H. Earle painted in 1943 which had previously belonged to the Subscription Library.

The earliest dated works by Hick were produced whilst in Scotland during and immediately after the First World War. A pencil drawing looking across the river Tay to the road bridge and town of Perth is inscribed 'Perth, Scotland 1918 Allanson Hick'.

A pair of countryside scenes also in the vicinity of Perth, in pencil, drawn on Reeves postcards, were produced the following year and one is entitled 'From roadside trough, Glasgow road, 20.7.1919' all of his other known works are post 1930. He met his wife in Scotland and there were regular trips north for many years after as evidenced by a pen and wash drawing dated 13 September 1959 of the Church of St. Serf, Dunning in Perthshire and another of Dunfermline Abbey, dated October 1964.

In 1930 Hick joined Dudley Harbron as partner in the architectural practice of Harbron and Hick of George Street, Hull. As far as the writer is aware Harbron never himself attempted any marine painting but possibly influenced by the younger man's enthusiasm for ships and sea he wrote an appreciation of the Hull marine artist John Ward (1798-1849) which was published in the *Burlington Magazine* during the War.[3] This brief but informative article was the first serious assessment of Ward's work to appear in print before Vincent Galloway's researches in to the local marine artist culminated in the 1951 Festival of Britain exhibition at the Ferens Art Gallery.

It is interesting to note that his grandfather John Harbron (1808-52), who was a decorator, painted the ceilings of the Hull Trinity House with a variety of shipping and nautical subjects.

Prior to the outbreak of the 1939-45 War the great four-masted barks of the Erikson fleet of Mariehamn, Finland, regularly sailed into Hull with cargoes of wheat from Australia, the last participants in the annual 'grain race'. They were a great delight for the artist and provided the subject for some outstanding drawings and paintings. In a letter written 6 November 1972 to Alex. A. Hurst the maritime author and publisher he reminisced about these now vanished sailing craft:[4]

'Dear Mr. Hurst
I did not anticipate your letter of October 17th so soon after ordering your book from Fischer Nautical at Brighton, but I was delighted to have your reply direct, with expectancy of its early publication.[5]

I regret that I have been unable to respond earlier, as I have been away from home during the past two weeks, in Edinburgh and again in London to the annual general meeting at the RSMA last week and to take a look at the exhibition at Guildhall. My somewhat remote Yorkshire location makes it impossible to visit as many of the functions as I would wish, but have frequently served on the selection and hanging committee, being a founder member in the past. I am indeed sorry to have missed meeting you this year.

The association with *Pommern* occurred during 1934 and 1939 when she twice came to Hull. I then made numerous studies when in port and my very first painting in the Royal Academy was of this subject, with bare poles in the dock. This drawing was reproduced and I will gladly send you a print or transparency if I can find one. Her second visit, when you left her in 1939, enabled me to see her in sail, in ballast as she left the Humber. I went with a photographer friend on the tug as far as the Bull lightship in order to obtain numerous shots from various angles and to watch her set sail. This was in July or August 1939. *Pommern* was the very last full-rigger to leave the Humber under sail.

Archibald Russell arrived about a week after this but from September 1939 she became a prominent target for frequent air raids. Consequently her top hamper was hastily removed. Sadly she was towed to Goole to spend declining years as a camouflaged naval storeship until her death in some breaker's yard. Fortunately I painted her on arrival in Hull which must be her final record.

After this period I applied for appointment as an official War Artist with the fleet or with auxiliaries and succeeded to obtain Admiralty permission to work privately within the area of Humber defences which gave me access to interesting activity which would have otherwise been prohibited.

Painting and drawing the nautical environment has been my passion throughout my life. My father was a shellback Cape Horner, later with command in the Ellerman Wilson Line and I have had sea experience ever since the age of 2 in 1900. Hence my early beginnings in an enthusiastic interest. Doubtless you will appreciate that very few nautical painters now remain who have ever seen a genuine four-masted barque. I knew most of the Erikson fleet of Mariehamn and this is the subject matter of your book, I gather, I am very anxious to see it. Still more anxious to meet you, if you can make this possible. When in London, now somewhat infrequently, I live at the Chelsea Arts Club, 143 Old Church Street, SW3. Could we arrange to meet there sometime? Perhaps you will be kind enough to write me if you have time. I knew Villiers[6] and Capt. de Claux and first met them aboard the *Parma*, I think during 1933.

Sincerely Yours, etc.

The photographic friend he mentions was the late Harry Cartlidge (1893-1987) who accompanied him on a number of visits to the docks and on the river. The Cartlidge collection comprising some twenty thousand photographic images is also now in the Town Docks Museum and includes pictures he took of the *Pommern* and *Archibald Russell*. There is also a delightful study of Hick standing at his easel on the deck of the *Parma*.

I have already referred to the drawing of the troopship *Empire Rapier* and this is shown tied up at a section of the Mulberry harbour which had been towed to Hull to use as a temporary replacement for the war damaged Riverside Quay. The original sketch was made in January 1947 aboard the motor launch *Kitty* skippered by her owner Charles Ayres and both he and Harry Cartlidge are referred to in the artist's inscription. The negatives of the photographs taken by the latter on the same occasion are also preserved in the museum collections.

Hick's close friend of many years standing was Harry Hudson Rodmell a notable poster artist and marine painter. He became a neighbour when Hick moved to Hornsea in 1941 after the blitz of Hull and during the period 1941-44 the latter was a member of the Home Guard and Rodmell had enrolled in the Royal Observer Corps. They had both been elected members of the Society of Graphic Artists in 1936 when Hick contributed six works for the SGA's exhibition in London in May of that year. Both men were founder members of the Society of Marine Artists (later the Royal Society of Marine Artists) and exhibited at the inaugural exhibition in 1946.[7]

Hick showed four watercolours, two of Danish seine netters in addition to 'Wartime dry dock' and '*Onslaught* refits'. The catalogue of the second annual exhibition, held at the Guildhall, records Hick both as a member of the Society's council (which included Norman Wilkinson and Harold Wyllie) and also as a member of the selection committee. Four items, all water colours, or drawings, were displayed in 1947 including '*Onslaught's* new shaft' which also appeared at the

Royal Academy the following year;[8] there are several variants of this subject in the museum collection. *The Visitor*, acquired in 1952 by the Bradford City Art Gallery was also shown as well as 'Trawler Slipway' and 'Leave boats at the Mulberry'; the latter subject sketched in the same year on the Humber is described above. A negative of the 'Trawler slipway' is in the Cartlidge collection along with a picture of a portrait sketch made by Hick of his photographer friend and of a drawing of the merchantman *City of Swansea* with a destroyer.

A steady flow of contributions for the annual exhibition of the RSMA was maintained but these studies were now greatly outnumbered by topographical and architectural scenes. In 1959 he made a design for a figure of Christ which was carved from wood by Clifford Langley for St. Paul's Church, Sculcoates. An attenuated figure, fourteen feet high, in a modernist style it was apparently Hick's only essay in the field of sculpture.[9] He drew subjects for the calendars of Richards, Hibbert and Co., later Oughtred and Harrison, which were mostly of familiar local buildings. Maritime examples did however include the *Tattershall Castle* off Victoria Pier and the continental car ferry at King George Dock.[10]

Hick's entrants for the 1972 RSMA exhibition comprised subjects old and new, a version of '*Onslaught's* new shaft' and 'Visitors for *Galatea*' appeared in the watercolour section. The Leander class frigate *Galatea* launched in 1963 was a regular visitor to Hull and in 1975 her officers and crew were granted the Freedom of the City. After scrapping in 1987 the ship's bell was presented to the Lord Mayor, Councillor Bowd, as Admiral of the Humber and it now hangs in the entrance to the Town Docks Museum.

Two oils were also displayed in 1972 'Dry dock' and 'Salvage by *Lloydsman*'. The latter vessel was built for United Towing of Hull in 1971 and in 1973 and 1975-6 was used as a Fishery Protection vessel during the Cod Wars before being sent to Singapore in 1979. Hick's friend Rodmell showed three pictures in the

RSMA exhibition for 1972 and Colin Verity the representative of a new generation of marine artist exhibited three drawings of trawlers.

Allanson Hick died at Hull Royal Infirmary in 1975[11] leaving a considerable cache of drawings and sketches in his studio and a well-chosen collection of canvasses, including works by Scottish artists such as Gemmell Hutchison and Ann Redpath. These remained in the possession of his widow[12] until her death in 1987 when some of the Scottish paintings were sold in April 1988 by Philips, Edinburgh and the portfolios of drawings shared among his nephews and nieces.

The last painting sent by him to the RSMA was in 1973 but a few months after his death the artist's diploma piece was displayed as a tribute to his memory at the annual exhibition. Occasional examples of Hick's work have passed through the sale rooms both locally and in London but by far the largest single group appeared at Phillips auction house in Leeds in 1988.[13]

The fourteen lots represented the residue of pictures which Hick's beneficiaries had decided to dispose of. The star item was the pencil and wash drawing of the *Pommern*, signed and dated 1935, the year it was exhibited at the Royal Academy. Bought by a dealer it was subsequently acquired by a Hull collector and is one of the items chosen for display at the Town Docks Museum.

An oil painting on panel entitled 'The Fish Dock Oiler' bore a label indicating that it had been hung at the RSMA and is possibly identical with the 'Dockside Oiler' seen at the Royal Academy in 1949. A watercolour sketch of this subject is also in the museum collection (M1.1920). Also at the sale was a lithograph of 'Bridgend, Perth' signed and dated 1932 and another prewar piece in the form of a pencil and wash drawing of 'Skipsea beach, looking towards Flamborough Head'. The remainder were various topographical views dated 1950-8 including Caernarvon Castle, St. Paul's, the nave altar Canterbury, Oxford, Compton Wyngates, Whites Club (St. James, SW1), an interior view of Hull Trinity House and St. Serf Church, Dunning, Perthshire.

A small commemmorative exhibition arranged by his friend Kenneth Hibbert, was held at the Ferens Art Gallery in 1976 made up of a selection of studies and finished drawings used for the annual calendar of Richards, Hibbert and Co. and Oughtred and Harrison, 1934-1974. Some of the originals have been lost over the years and some were given away, one of King Billy (the gilded equestrian statue of William 3 in Market Place) was given to the manager of the Corn Exchange and taken by him to Australia. Another, of the new police station in Queen's Gardens was given to Mr. Sidney Lawrence, the then Chief Constable. About one thousand of these calendars were produced each year and distributed world-wide; a list of the subjects displayed at the Ferens is given in an appendix.[14]

In 1988 Oughtred and Harrison disposed of the complete collection to a gallery since when a group of these pictures was sold on May 15, 1990 by H. Evans and Sons, Hull.

I am indebted to Alan Bray for the biographical sketch which follows this introduction. From 1936 to 1940 he was an articled pupil in the office of G. Dudley Harbron and Allanson Hick, Architects of Bond Street, Hull. His family had always had a close association with the Hick family, his father and grandfather and Allanson Hick's father were all seafarers in the service of the Wilson Line. He writes from perhaps a unique knowledge of his subject.

Alan Bray retired as senior partner with Hull architects Gelder and Kitchen in 1981 but he still draws and paints and exhibits his work locally.

Additional information and enthusiastic support for the exhibition has been provided by Alexander 'Sandy' Chamberlain who is a keen advocate of his uncle's work.

Pencil sketch, Perth, 1918.

'From roadside irough, Glasgow Road, 20.7.1919'. Pencil sketch made on the outskirts of Perth.

*Four-masted bark **Parma** in Hull docks, 1935.*

'It is generally known that I have a somewhat excitable nature and can be relied upon to warm up readily, even to an explosive condition, and indulge in the most provoking statements especially if the subject is one about which I have intensive feelings.'[15]

Thus, Allanson Hick in a fifties debate on aesthetics, and to those who knew him the self description is certainly accurate. But, he had those intensive feelings upon very many subjects, no doubt the most intensive in the sphere of art and architecture. The *Architects' Journal* in its review of Hull architectural practices in July 1953 described him as 'Blunt and jovial, and with great enthusiasm, he is a good and witty speaker, save, perhaps, for the chip which he tends to carry on his shoulder'. A large man, patient and impatient by turns, he loved to expound his very heart felt and trenchant opinions to anybody who would listen and to some that would not.

Born on 19th June, 1898 at 89 Walton Street, his family were all seafaring. His grandfather, born in Hull in 1826, commanded and navigated wooden billy boys and brigs, and there were also family connections with West Hartlepool. His father, Captain Allanson Hick, had a long and distinguished career serving in fifteen of the Wilson Line's ships, beginning in 1884 as second officer of the *Marsdin,* and progressing through a series of vessels as chief officer until his first command (of the *Polo)* in 1897. Next door in Walton Street lived their relatives the Boxhalls (Joe Boxhall it was who became fourth officer of the ill-fated *Titanic).* His mother, Alice Hick (nee Groves) also came from a seafaring family. With all this maritime background, a sea career might have been confidently anticipated for the young Allanson (his father would call him 'Ally' which he hated), but, this was not to be. In 1905 the family moved to 38 Albany Street and young Allanson progressed through the Misses Wetherill's prep school in Park Street, to the Hull Grammar School.

When war broke out in 1914, he was just sixteen years of age, and it must have already been decided that a sea career was not for him since boys were usually entered at the Trinity House Navigation School at 13 years of age. In fact, Allanson Hick became an architect's pupil in the office of Wheatley and Houldsworth. Not long after this, against his parents' wishes, he enlisted in Kitchener's new army, under age.

His father, in command of the *Rondo* at the outbreak of war, became master of the *Urbino.* On the 24th of September, 1915, *Urbino* was sunk by gunfire off the Bishop Rock, but Captain Hick and his crew survived. His next ship, the *Erato,* was his last command, for he retired on the 26th June, 1916, at the age of 60.[16]

Meanwhile, his son was serving in the East Yorkshire Regiment and saw service both in the Near East and on the Western Front. At some time, he became either attached to or transferred to the Royal Scots' Regiment and it was during this period, probably after the Armistice, but before his demobilisation that he met in Perth, Sarah Knight McCowan who was to become his wife. Miss McCowan, fourth of a family of five children, always known as Sadie, eventually became Mrs. Hick, but not until 1926. The marriage took place in Perth on 17th April, the day before Sadie's birthday. She was then 25 and Allanson nearly 28. By 1929 they were living at 82 Albany Street, Hull. In those years after the war, Allanson Hick had been assiduously working in Hull as an architectural assistant, again with Wheatley and Houldsworth and later with the larger firm of Gelder and Kitchen.

No doubt this office practice was assisted by evening studies. On August 21st in 1921, a meeting had taken place at the Hull Young People's Institute, at which it was decided to form, in rooms rented at the Metropole Hall, West Street, the Hull Atelier of Architecture, whose activities were eventually transferred to the College of Art. It was from these beginnings that we may be sure attendance by Allanson Hick provided early study and interest in both architecture and in drawing and painting. In fact, he rapidly became a very competent architect and draughtsman, a considerable asset to any architectural practice. His early domestic and commercial design work included new offices (Dundee Chambers) for the Dundee, Perth and London Shipping Company in Princes Dock Side, which he designed while an assistant in the office of W. B. Blanchard in 1928, and other buildings in Hull some of which have been destroyed or subsequently demolished upon redevelopment.

Mr Blanchard, in addition to his architectural practice, also carried on a business as estate agent, but Allanson Hick, now a Licentiate of the Royal Institute of British Architects, and always the true professional, hated this mix of activities and looked for advancement in a practice partnership. In 1930, this was made possible by the beginning of his partnership with G. Dudley Harbron, then aged about 50, a man of considerable intellect, an author, regular contributor to the *Architects' Journal,* lecturer at the local School of Architecture and with a long record of professional architectural practice. Harbron and Hick began practice from Halifax Chambers, 32 George Street, Hull.

With more freedom, and in a period when, as with everything else in the early thirties, architectural work was stagnant, Allanson Hick found plenty of opportunity to draw and paint and this became the beginning of his most prolific period.

In the sphere of art his earlier heroes were William Walcot, Claude Muncaster and Muirhead Bone.[17] Widening interests in the more colourful moderns came later, such as the Scottish colourists. These interests were reflected in his own eventual collection of paintings which included works by Walcot, Philip Connard, Gemmell Hutchison and Ann Redpath.[18]

On the 9th August 1967 for instance Aitken Dott and Son, The Scottish Gallery, Edinburgh, offered him a fine Walcot:

Dear Mr. Hick,

Are you feeling rich and are you to be tempted with the finest Walcot we have yet had? It is "Waterloo Bridge" 21 x 23" illustrated in colour on page iv of the Walcot book. The price is £120 and you are the first of our Walcot admirers to whom I have offered it. It is in its original frame and was catalogued no. 14 in the Fine Art Society exhibition in December 1919. It really is a superb Walcot.

Yours sincerely
William J. Macaulay

He bought the picture which on 11 May 1988 was sold as lot 121 by Philips, Leeds, for £4,600.

This sale also included his other three Walcots (122, 124 and 191) with other paintings from his collection.

The Walcot book mentioned in the letter was *The Architectural Watercolours and Etchings of William Walcot* published in 1919 in a limited edition of 250 copies with an introduction by Sir Reginald Blamfield.

His skill and technique matured until in 1935 he was able to claim his first major success by having his watercolour of the Finnish barque *Pommern* and another entitled 'Dockland' exhibited at the Royal Academy. He then regularly exhibited works at the academy until 1955, three-quarters of which were marine subjects. It was structure which always interested him and which he loved to draw and paint, whether the structure of ships, docks or cranes or of buildings. The bare poles of his sailing ships offered this opportunity as with the linear presentation of buildings. He proposed a series of 'Bridges in the North' and had already drawn the bridge at Perth, and also the Forth and Tyne bridges. Scaffolding on buildings always fascinated him and he drew St. Lawrence, Jewry London with festoons of scaffolding. 'Trees in winter garb are always more preferable to me than in summer' he told one of his audiences, for he gave talks to many local societies and expounded his always very strong views on presentation, taste and artistic appreciation. He was a great admirer of Renaissance architecture, but also of the Gothic period. One of his pet hates was the sham half timber building prevalent in the thirties, in fact anything sham or insincere aroused his passionate criticism.

In 1935 he drew his first calendar for the Insurance Brokers, Richards, Hibbert and Co. Ltd. His original drawing made for this calendar, which showed the firm's offices in Queen Victoria Square, next to the Ferens Art Gallery, was acquired by the Hull City Council in 1989 for the Ferens collection. This was to be the first of a long series of calendars which included in 1938 a drawing of Prince's Dock, the original of which was purchased at the time by the then Hull Corporation for the permanent collection.

He undertook in 1936, a skilful conversion of two three-storied Georgian terraced houses in Bond Street, Nos. 3 and 4, to accommodate, on the ground floor, what was to become the famous Jenny's Cafe, under the direction of his sister-in-law, Jenny Chamberlain. On the upper floors were three flats and some office accommodation. The design of the cafe included not just the building work, but the fittings and furnishings – tables and chairs in limed oak, blue-grey folk weave curtains and upholstery, decor in pale buff and dull blue, a carved and embossed stone slab bearing the blue coffee pot sign at the entrance, and even the menu headings. Publicity material was ably contributed by his erudite friend Kenneth Hibbert. The practice of Harbron and Hick moved into accommodation on the first floor.

Not far away in Kingston Square, Peppino Santangelo's 'Little Theatre' flourished. The Repertory company found the cafe in Bond Street a home-from-home and regular meeting place, and its producer, Jack Minster, took up residence in one of its flats. Jenny's became a veritable Arts Centre. The Hull Art Club, formed in 1932, now made Jenny's its headquarters. Paintings hung around the walls, many were by Allanson Hick. The *Hull Daily Mail* in a review of an Art Club Exhibition referred to 'the Bond Street School'. Allanson Hick subsequently presented a comprehensive history of Bond Street in a talk given to the Antiquarian Society.[19]

From the bow front window of Jenny's Cafe, on Saturday mornings, a fine view of the wedding parties emerging from the Registry Office opposite, could be had, to the strains of 'Me and the Moon' from the barrel organ strategically positioned near the cafe entrance until its Italian owner (plus monkey) were suitably bribed, usually by Allanson Hick, to depart.

The partnership of Harbron and Hick was not always a particularly smooth running one. The two were very unlike. Dudley Harbron, slight, balding and donnish, considered himself to be a genius. 'A genius', he said 'had the ability to reconcile opposites'. He could reconcile opposites, he declared, therefore he was a genius. 'come, come Dudley', Allanson would say. But, Dudley Harbron with a scornful glance rearwards, would stamp off down the stairs, bowler hat at a suitably genius angle, and roll of plans under arm, leaving a gleeful Allanson Hick. Nevertheless, he greatly admired Dudley Harbron as an architect and literary man.

In 1936, both Allanson Hick and his great friend, Harry Hudson Rodmell, himself a frequent visitor to Bond Street, were elected members of the Society of Graphic Artists. Allanson Hick's main interest as well as in architectural subjects, continued to be in drawing and painting of ships and docklands. Around this time, he began to explore other media, including etching, lithography and oil painting, the latter particularly by the palette knife method. His ever present nautical interest was particularly in the four-masted Finnish barques which sailed into Hull docks at fairly regular intervals. When one of these arrivals was signalled, Allanson Hick's office work was abruptly dropped as he hastened to the dockside, burdened with his sketching equipment. On many occasions, he and Harry Cartlidge, another good friend and well known photographer, would sail on the tug as far as Spurn to bring the ship up-river to dock, or outward bound. The many sailing ships which formed this subject matter were almost always shown in dock with sails furled. He liked to present them looming up large and with dramatic effect. People would say – but you've not shown all the top foremast – or all of the bowsprit (this would make him furious).

Portraiture seized his imagination around the later thirties, and he embaked on a series of portraits including one of Captain Rowntree of Hull Trinity House, F. R. Bell, former master of the Hull Grammar School and many others. Also, in the latter forties, he produced notable railway posters, possibly encouraged by his friend Rodmell whose own posters were and are well known.

Before the war, the Society of Marine Artists (now the R.S.M.A.) was formed. Allanson Hick and Hudson Rodmell were founder members. An inaugural exhibition in October 1939, had to be cancelled due to the outbreak of war, but both showed pictures in the United Artists Exhibition at Burlington House and the Royal Academy exhibition opened as usual in 1940 and included two works by Allanson Hick. Wartime stimulated rather than curtailed his output of work and soon after the commencement of hostilities he obtained permission from the Admiralty to work privately within the area of Humber Defences which gave him access to interesting activity which would otherwise have been prohibited.

In 1941, following repeated severe bombing in Hull, the Hicks moved house to 19 Grosvenor Terrace (now New Road), Hornsea and Allanson Hick joined the local Home Guard. The practice in Hull continued, though with limited architectural work, mostly war damage reports, war time hostels, etc. Jenny's cafe, although damaged, continued to function, surrounded by debris and flattened buildings, and with its basement strengthened by heavy timbers.

During 1942, Allan found time to teach at the School of Architecture, then in temporary wartime premises in Park Street. Thus, Dudley Harbron in a letter written at this time: 'Hick attends in the morning, twice a week. He is improving as a teacher – but his principal defect is that he will try to replan everything himself – instead of improving or correcting the pupils' plans or designs. If his idea were to prevail, all the plans would be alike, and all would be as he imagined they should be'.

In this war period, it would appear that Allanson Hick was concentrating his attention on naval shipping, including much work shown in the present exhibition. These had to be submitted for approval by the naval authority and directions for omission of features or numbers considered to be of possible help to the enemy were frequent – and the naval censor's large pencil directions are frequently in evidence.

After the war, Allanson Hick's return to more normal life is shown by the dilution of his shipping subject matter with more architectural or other subjects. Frequent visits to London, where he stayed at his club, the Chelsea Arts, in connection with the various exhibitions at which he was a contributor gave him opportunity for working on the architectural subjects which he loved, the London scene, the clubs, Boodles, Whites and others, the Haymarket Theatre, the Horse Guards, All Souls, Lengham Place and the B.B.C., rebuilding in the City including St. Paul's and so on. In 1946, he was showing work at the Royal Academy, the Society of Marine Artists, even at the Paris Salon de Marine.

In 1949 the partnership with Dudley Harbron was dissolved, but Allanson Hick, now a Fellow of the Royal Institute of British Architects, continued to work from 4 Bond Street. At the end of the war, his office became much more like a painter's studio and much less like an architect's office. He moved to 24 Albion Street in 1961 when the Bond Street premises were compulsorily acquired for redevelopment, and regretfully the much loved Jenny's cafe closed for ever.

In 1954-5 he was President of the prestigious York and East Yorkshire Architectural Society. His architectural work was, of course, continuing, one of his more important works being the new Telephone Exchange in Newbegin, Beverley (1954-56), and he also had domestic and some church work on hand. In

1958 he was elected a member of the Art Workers' Guild.

After the war, the calendars for Richards, Hibbert & Co., later part of the Oughtred & Harrison Insurance Group, continued and the subject for his last calendar but one in Christmas 1972, was the Dock Offices, now the Town Docks Museum.

Included in the exhibition is only a small proportion of his lifetime's vast output of work, but many might conclude from it that his on the spot sketches and drawings surpass in quality and impact that of his finished work.

Allanson Hick died on 11th May, 1975. His wife died on 20th October, 1987. They had no children.

*The artist working at his easel on board the **Parma**.*

NOTES

1. See Town Docks Museum - Permanent Collection.

2. See Ferens Art Gallery - Permanent Collection.

3. G. Dudley Harbron 'John Ward, painter, 1798-1849' *Burlington Magazine*, October 1941, pp.130-4; Vincent Galloway *Early Marine Painters and Hull Art Directory*, Ferens Art Gallery, Hull, 1951 (exhibition catalogue); and A. G. Credland *John Ward of Hull, Marine Painter, 1798-1849*, Ferens Art Gallery, Hull. 1981.

4. Courtesy of Mr. A. G. Chamberlain.

5. A. A. Hurst, *Square-riggers, the final epoch, 1921-58*, Fischer Nautical/Teredo Books, Brighton, 1972.

6. Alan J. Villiers, born in Australia 23 September 1903 was one of the members of the consortium which purchased the *Parma* in 1931 (Capt. De Claux was master). A prolific author he wrote of his lifetime experience at sea and was nautical adviser during the making of the films of *Moby Dick* and *Billy Budd*. He died 3 March 1982 aged 78 (see *The Times*, 5 March 1982, p.14).

7. For Rodmell see A. G. Credland *Harry Hudson Rodmell - Marine Artist, 1896-1984*, Town Docks Museum, Hull, 1984 (exhibition booklet). The chief instigator of the formation of the Society of Marine Artists was another Yorkshireman, Charles Pears (1873-1958). Born in Pontefract he became a professional illustrator and was an official war artist in 1914-8. He also worked for the War Artists' Commission in 1939-45.

8. See Pictures loaned for exhibition.

9. *Hull Times*, January 31st 1959, p.1.

10. See appendix 2.

11. A short obituary appeared in the *Humberside Bystander*, June 1975, vol.11, no.2, pp.38-9, written by J. L. Harrison who had been at school with Hick as a child under the guidance of the Misses Weatherill.

12. As a tribute to her husband Mrs. Hick was made an Honorary Lay Member of the Royal Society of Marine Artists in 1976.

13. *Phillips* (Leeds), Wednesday 17 February 1988, pt.2, drawings and watercolours, lots 163-176.

14. A photocopied handlist was available at the time.

15. From a talk given 11 February 1953; a transcript is in the possession of Mr. Bray.

16. Master for the first time in 1897 he retired after over thirty years' service, nineteen in command.

17. Claude G. Muncaster (1903-74); had professional experience at sea including a spell in the four-masted bark *Olivebank,* one of Erikson's grain ships sailing out of Mariehamn and another visitor to Hull. A particular feature of his work were splendid deck scenes aboard sailing vessels. Muncaster was president of the RSMA after the death of Charles Pears in 1957.

    Sir Muirhead Bone (1876-1953), draughtsman and engraver was an official war artist in 1914-18 and worked for the War Artists' Commission in 1939-45.

    William Walcot (1874-1943), architect and graphic artist, born in Odessa.

18. Phillip Connard (1875-1958), painter and designer; he painted murals for the *Queen Mary* and on a miniature scale in the Queen's dolls house at Windsor.

    Robert Gemmell Hutchison (1855-1936), Scottish painter of genre and portraits, born in Edinburgh. Ann Redpath (1895-1965); Scottish painter in oils and watercolours of landscape and still life.

19. The East Riding Antiquarian Society.

Portrait of Harry Cartlidge, photographer, 7.2.1941.

*Photograph by Harry Cartlidge of **Pommern** under tow.*

JENNY'S
4. BOND STREET.
HULL.

LUNCHEONS
SNACKS
MORNING COFFEE
TEA
HOME MADE
CAKES, SWEETS & CONFECTIONERY.

You have probably deplored the lack of individuality which characterises so much of modern life.

Everywhere we go we find a sameness which is nauseating to the sensitive mind. The little village store, with its essential individuality, has gone and its place has been taken by the multiple shop, —a shallow and vulgar mockery, where ''Service'' is a catch-word and cellophane mistaken for wholesomeness. Where tinned foods take the place of rich farm produce and quack medicines the place of brimstone and treacle. Life today lacks reality.

And that's what Jenny thought.

So in Bond Street she has opened an eating house for the discriminating palate. Not a Restaurant where anyone can have a standard meal, but a tasteful house where good foods, coffee and thick rich cream and tea - tea that makes Chinamen think of home and Indians long for their mothers— is served to people who like real food and drink.

A small, intimate house where good food is served with a rich individuality and a dash of Scottish sincerity.

Come and see Jenny's for yourself.

An advertisement for Jenny's,
typed on headed notepaper. c.1936.

The late and much lamented Jenny's Cafe,
Bond Street, Hull.

(1) M1.1848. *Pencil and wash.* Portion of the Mulberry harbour, the artificial harbour constructed off the Normandy beaches for the invasion in 1944, used as a temporary replacement for the war-damaged Riverside quay. Marked up with colour notes and the inscription as follows 'The Humber Mulberry Old Riverside Quay LNER, Cuxhaven leave boat *Empire Rapier* with H. C. and Chas. Ayres Jan. 1st 1947.

H. C. is Harry Cartlidge who often accompanied Allanson Hick on trips along the river. Charles Ayres ran a motor launch called *Kitty* which served as a river taxi. (Presented by A. G. Chamberlain).   8.$^1/_4$ x 11in.

(2) M1.1849.   *Pencil drawing* (squared up on layout paper). Derived from the preceding and preliminary to final oil painting. (Presented by A. G. Chamberlain).   13$^1/_2$ x 18in.

Items M1.1862-M1.1937; purchased 1990:- All executed on cartridge paper unless stated otherwise.

(3) M1.1862. *Watercolour* (pencil drawing visible beneath). Port side view of: 'Corvette HMS *Killegray,* Princes Dock, Hull, new commissioned Sat. Nov. 8th, 1941. Allanson Hick'; 'No.1 Lt. H. L. Mallitte RNVR'. The *Killegray* was an Isles Class naval trawler built at the Beverley Yard of Cook, Welton and Gemmell in 1941. It passed under the command of the Royal New Zealand Navy in 1942 and was scrapped in 1958. The vessel bears the pennant number T.174 and the sheet is inscribed on the back by the censor, 'take out pendant number, name of ship not to be mentioned'.
10$^1/_2$ x 14$^1/_2$in.

(4) M1.1863. *Watercolour.* Starboard bow section and bridge of HMS *Inkpen* at dockside. Inscribed 'Camouflaged Corvette, Hull June 17, 1942, HMS *Inkpen,* Allanson Hick'.

Hills class naval trawler, T225, built at the Beverley Yard of Cook, Welton and Gemmell and launched in December 1941. After the war she fished under the name of *Stella Capella* (Charleson Smith Trawlers Ltd.) and was scrapped in 1963.

Censor's pencil instruction to block out pendant number and inscribed on the back 'sketch to be amended as indicated, *Inkpen* is a trawler not a corvette. No name of place to be given'.   12$^3/_4$ x 16$^1/_2$in.

(5) M1.1864. *Watercolour* (on tinted paper). Port profile of vessel alongside dock with jib crane; camouflage pattern on hull. Inscribed '*Wheatland* new type escort LI22. Fitting Wm. Wright dock, August 1942 Allanson Hick'.

An escort destroyer built at the Yarrow yard in 1941. On the 1-2 November 1944 *Wheatland* and *Avon Vale* working along the Dalmatian coast encountered the former Italian torpedo boat TA20 and two escort vessels and sank them all.

It was a hulk in 1955 and scrapped at Boness four years later.

Censor's pencil instructions to black out the pennant number and the radar/radio aerials on the mast. Inscribed on the back 'sketch must be amended as indicated, name of place to be erased'.   12$^1/_4$ x 16$^1/_4$in.

(6) M1.1865.   *Pencil drawing* (on squared-up layout paper). Starboard bow view *Woodruff* corvette.
9$^3/_4$ x 13$^1/_4$in.

(7) M1.1866.   *Pencil drawing* (on squared-up layout paper). Enlarged version of M1.1865. Inscribed '*Woodruff* corvette from private photograph $^1/_4$in. sq. to 1in. Also taken to 1$^1/_4$in. for 16/12 mount. Lieut. Dukes (Canada) Lieut. Yelland.

A Flower class corvette, K.53, launched in February 1941; transferred to the merchant marine in 1948 as the *Southern Lupin* and scrapped at Odense in 1959.
9$^1/_2$ x 15in.

(8) M1.1867. *Watercolour and crayon sketch.* Starboard view marked with colour instructions. Inscribed 'Shackletons *Quest* St. Andrews Dock, Hull, July 6th, 1944, 12.50-13.10pm 20 mins. water carrier for corvettes based at Immingham, Allanson Hick'.

Built in 1917 the *Quest* was purchased by Sir Ernest Shackleton for the Antarctic expedition of 1920-1 she was originally the Norwegian whaler *Foca I*. Used in 1928 in the search for General Nobile and the crew of the airship *Italia* after its ill-fated attempt to fly over the North Pole. Chartered 1930-1 by British Arctic Air Route expedition to Greenland, she was finally lost off Labrador in May 1962.

Censor's note 'place name will not be given' after inscription and blue stamp on the reverse 'No Admiralty objection A.R.R. Captain RN' 'Passed for publication Oct. 19' There is also a portrait head in pencil, drawn on the reverse. $11^1/_2$ x $15^1/_2$in.

(9) M1.1868. *Watercolour and charcoal.* Two vessels, one a converted trawler, tied up at the dockside and bearing the serial letters MO and GA.

Each is fitted with an A-frame on the bows and an acoustic hammer. The loud noise exploded acoustically detonated mines harmlessly ahead of the ship otherwise the vessel's engines would trigger the mine when directly overhead. These two craft may have been used to clear mines off the Normandy coast in preparation for the invasion.

Inscribed in upper margin 1605-1635 *Montano* and *Garola*. Red and blue official stamps on the back 'Not to be published – Ministry of Information 1944'.
$8^3/_4$ x $13^3/_4$in.

(10) M1.1869. *Watercolour and ink.* Port bow view at dockside, inscribed 'Sloop U36 refitting. Fish Dock, Hull, 1943 Allanson Hick'

A Grimsby class sloop built at Devonport in 1933 HMS *Leith* was originally given the pennant number L36. She survived the war and was renamed *Byron*, 1946, in the merchant marine. Renamed *Friendship* in 1948 and

became the RDN *Galathea* in 1949. Scrapped in 1955. Inscribed on reverse, 'sketch to be amended as indicated, name of place to be erased'. $12^1/_4$ x $17^1/_4$in.

(11) M1.1870. *Crayon or pastel sketch* (on tinted paper; touches of watercolour). Two vessels of war tied up side-by-side in dock. 11 x 15in.

(12) M1.1871. *Watercolour* Amidships of vessel of war tied up at dockside. Gangway down and figures ashore and on board. Torpedo tubes visible on upper works and extensive radio and radar aerials.

Inscribed in the left margin 'Blue shield, white circle with red ring, gold 10'. This refers to insignia on funnel. $12^1/_2$ x 18in.

(13) M1.1872. *Watercolour* (on board). Inscribed *Demodocus* KGV dock Hull Sept. 10 1949'.

The ss *Demodocus* was built in 1912 for the China Mutual Steam Navigation Co., managed by A. Holt, registered in Liverpool and is here shown in King George Dock, Hull. $11^3/_4$ x $13^3/_4$in.

(14) M1.1873. *Watercolour* (on board; squared up). Battle-scarred destroyer in dock; inscribed in upper margin '. . . pencil 12/4 . . . and colour 2-4.30 Thurs. Feb. 11, 1943. Sat. 13th 2.30-4pm. In lower margin 'SS 161/2 - 12 "the wounded *Onslow*". Refitting. Hull K.G. Dock 1943, Allanson Hick'.

This O class destroyer, G17, was built by John Brown on the Clyde in 1941. On the 27 December 1941 she took part in the Vaagso raid and on 14 September 1942 sank U88 while escorting convoy PQ18.

This was the first Russian convoy after the disastrous PQ17 which had scattered under threat of attack by the *Tirpitz* and had been virtually annihilated. Another furious attack was rebuffed and although ten merchant vessels were lost a total of 41 German aircraft were shot down. They had flown more than three hundred sorties but failed to break up the convoy and *Scheer*, *Hipper*

Sketches made on the back of the Jenny's advertisement.

*Sketch on deck of **Parma,** 1933 (Cat. 64).*

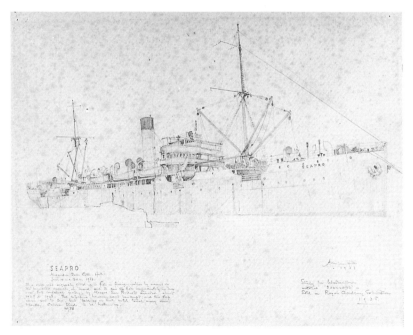

*Fish processing vessel **Seapro** in Alexandra dock 1933 (Cat. 79).*

and *Köhn* thankfully remained in Norway throughout the battle.

In December 1942 while accompanying convoy JW51B from Scotland to Russia she engaged the 10,000 ton German cruiser *Admiral Hipper*. The latter temporarily broke off and sank the destroyer *Achates* before exchanging further shots. The *Onslow* suffered considerable damage and her commanding officer Capt. R. St. V. Sherbrooke was severely injured in the face. The pocket battleship *Lutzow* then made an appearance but fortunately the cruisers *Sheffield* and *Jamaica* also arrived on the scene and the German vessels made their departure.

Onslow came into the King George Dock at Hull where she remained until mid-April undergoing extensive repairs. Capt. Sherbrooke was awarded the VC for his determined action against superior forces while suffering from severe wounds.

In December 1943 *Onslow* was part of a protective screen for the homeward bound convoy RA5SAS and JW55B sailing east. The escort of fourteen destroyers and three smaller vessels successfully protected their charges despite the appearance of the battle cruiser *Scharnhorst*. The latter was pursued by the accompanying cruisers and finally sunk by the battleship *Duke of York* on the 26th December.

In company with the *Offa* on 18 June 1944, the *Onslow* beat off seven JU88 bombers and on 11-12 July 1945 with other units engaged an enemy convoy off Norway sinking a minesweeper, tanker and several other vessels. As leader of the 17th destroyer flotilla in 1946 she was responsible for taking out to sea groups of captured U-boats which were sunk with demolition charges and gunfire. Sold to the Royal Pakistan Navy in 1949 she was renamed *Tippu Sultan*.

The drawing is marked with the censor's pencil instruction to block out the aerial and is inscribed on the reverse 'This sketch must be altered as amended. Caption also to be amended, no mention of ship or place'. $12^3/_4$ x 17in.

(15) M1.1874. *Watercolour and pen and ink.* Rear port side view of destroyer *Onslaught* in dry dock. $12^1/_2$ x 17in.

(16) M1.1875. *Watercolour* (laid down on board). View of rear port side of destroyer *Faulkner* seen from floor of the dock (see below for description). $13^1/_4$ x $17^3/_4$in.

(17) M1.1876. *Pencil and sepia sketch* (squared up layout paper). The *Onslaught;* same view as M1.1874. $12^1/_2$ x 16in.

M1.1877. *Pencil sketch* (layout paper; squared-up). Destroyer *Onslaught*. Same design as M1.1874. Painting instruction in bottom right hand corner. $20^3/_4$ x 31in.

(18) M1.1878. *Watercolour.* Destroyer *Onslaught.* (Same design as M1.1874 etc.). Censor's stamp on reverse. 'Press and censorship bureau'. 'Not to be published.' $12^3/_4$ x $21^1/_4$in.

(19) M1.1879. *Watercolour.* Destroyer at dockside. Sailors on gang plank; jib crane and mobile generator. 13 x $17^1/_2$in.

(20) M1.1880. *Watercolour.* Destroyer amidships, at dockside. $13^1/_4$ x 18in.

M1.1881. *Crayon and wash.* Bow, port side view of destroyer with camouflaged hull; at dockside. 12 x $15^1/_2$in.

M1.1882. *Watercolour.* Initial study of M1.1879. $11^3/_4$ x 16in.

(21) M1.1883. *Watercolour.* Bow port side view of destroyer, camouflaged hull; chipping and scraping. Signed Allanson Hick, bottom right hand corner. $12^1/_2$ x 18in.

M1.1884. *Pencil and wash.* Rough sketch of preceding item (M1.1883) with colour instructions. Dated 26.10.1943. Stamp on back, 'No Admiralty objection – passed for publication 1 March 1944, etc.'. $12^1/_2$ x $17^1/_4$in.

(22) M1.1885. *Watercolour* (squared up). Bow view of destroyer *Onslaught*, GO4, in dry dock.

O class destroyer *Onslaught* built by Fairfield and launched 9 October 1941. She was part of the 3rd Escort Group in the North Atlantic in Spring 1943. This was the height of the U-boat campaign and in the first twenty days of March nearly one hundred merchant vessels were lost, in all waters, amounting to a half million tons of shipping and nearly two thirds of these were in convoy. *Onslaught* and her sisters of the O class saw intensive action throughout the war but though damaged and disabled not a single one was lost during the entire period of hostilities.

In March 1944 she was part of the escort to the westward bound convoy RA57 from Russia comprising thirty-one ships. No less than fifteen U-boats were ranged against them but only one merchantman was sunk and *Onslaught* gave the coup de grace to U472 damaged by a rocket-firing Swordfish aircraft. In 1951 she was sold to the Royal Pakistan Navy and renamed *Tughril*.

Censor's stamp on the back 'not to be published'. $14^3/_4$ x 19in.

M1.1886. *Crayon* (squared up). Destroyer, port profile. On reverse censor's stamp 'Passed . . . 1 Jan. 1945'. $11^1/_2$ x 18in.

M1.1887. *Pencil tracing.* Amidships of destroyer *(Onslaught)*. $8^1/_4$ x 12in.

(23) M1.1888. *Crayon or pastel sketch.* Bridge of destroyer. Inscribed '*Onslaught* Trials Nov. 3 1944 Allanson Hick'. $8^3/_4$ x $13^3/_4$in.

(24) M1.1889. *Crayon or pastel sketch.* From deck of destroyer. Inscribed '*Onslaught* trial Nov. 3 1944 Allanson Hick'.
Censor's stamp on back 'No Admiralty objection – passed for publication 1 January 1945'. $18^1/_2$ x $13^3/_4$in.

(25) M1.1890. *Pencil drawing.* Inscribed '*Onslaught* trial Nov. 3 1944. Doc in Wardroom. Allanson Hick'. Passed for publication 1 Jan. 1945. $8^3/_4$ x $13^3/_4$in.

(26) M1.1891. *Pencil drawing.* Figure on deck of destroyer. Inscribed '*Onslaught* trial Nov. 3 1944, No.1 (Olly). Allanson Hick'.
Passed for publication 1 Jan. 1945. $8^1/_2$ x $13^1/_4$in.

(27) M1.1892. *Pencil drawing.* On board destroyer, looking forward. Inscribed '*Onslaught* trial Nov. 3 1944. Allanson Hick'. $8^3/_4$ x $13^1/_4$in.

M1.1893. *Crayon or pastel sketch.* Looking from deck of destroyer; depth charges in racks. Inscribed '*Onslaught* trial Nov. 3 1944'. 9 x 14in.

M1.1894. *Crayon or pastel sketch.* From deck of destroyer; a merchantman in distance. Inscribed '*Onslaught*, trial Nov. 3, 1944'. $8^3/_4$ x $13^3/_4$in.

M1.1895. *Crayon or pastel sketch.* Destroyer gun mounting. Inscribed '*Onslaught* trial Nov. 3 1944. $8^3/_4$ x $13^3/_4$in.

(28) M1.1896. *Pencil sketch.* Bow port side view of HMS *Milne.* Badge of *Onslaught*, with colour instructions alongside.
M class destroyer *Milne*, G14, was launched in December 1941. In September 1942 while *Onslow* was leader of force A of the squadron protecting the Russian convoy PQ18 the *Milne* was leader of B force which also included *Faulknor* (see below). She survived hostilities and was sold to the Turkish navy in 1958, renamed *Alp Arslan*. $8^3/_4$ x $13^3/_4$in.

*Four-masted steel bark **Parma** of Mariehamn, built in 1902 at Port Glasgow (Cat. 42).*

M1.1897. *Pencil tracing* (squared up). Destroyer *Onslaught* oiling. 15 x 21in.

(29) M1.1898. *Watercolour* (laid down on board). Destroyer amidships alongside dock. Inscribed 'Study during refit 1943. Destroyer *Milne* in fitting basin'. $12^1/_2$ x $17^1/_2$in.

(30) M1.1899. *Watercolour*. Stern view of three O class destroyers side by side, *Onslow* G17, *Offa* G29, *Onslaught* G04.
Offa was built by Fairfield and launched 9 October 1949. She was part of the squadron protecting the Russian convoy PQ18 in September 1942, a force which included *Milne, Faulknor, Onslow, Onslaught* and *Opportune*. The *Milne* was sold to the Turkish navy in 1949 and renamed *Tariq*. $12^1/_2$ x $16^1/_2$in.

M1.1900. *Pen and wash*. Bow view of destroyer at dockside. Inscribed 'Destroyer *Offa*, taking in ammunition. Study of bows and camouflage. Allanson Hick.
Censor's stamp on back 'No Admiralty Objections'. $10^3/_4$ x $14^3/_4$in.

(31) M1.1901. *Crayon and wash*. Destroyer; inscribed '*Bedouin* Tribal class destroyer, William Wright dock, Hull. Sat. May 30th 1942. Allanson Hick 3.45 - 4.15pm'.
The Tribal class destroyer *Bedouin* G67 (originally F.67) was at Narvik in April 1940 and with her fellow Tribal, the *Eskimo* torpedoed the German destroyer *Koellner* and scored hits on the destroyer *Georg Thiele* when in company with *Forester, Hero* and *Icarus*. Shortly after the date when the drawing was made she joined the Harpoon convoy in June 1942 heading for Malta to revictual the beleaguered island. She and four other destroyers left the convoy to engage the Italian cruisers *Raimondo Montecuccoli* and *Eugenio di Savoia* and was severely disabled. After being taken under tow by HMS *Partridge* she was sunk on 15 June by a

torpedo bomber which was brought down with the vessel's last shots. Cdr. B. G. Scairfield and his crew were rescued and imprisoned in Italy.
Censor's pencil instruction to block out the pendant, number and the radar dish. Note on the reverse 'This sketch must be altered and amended, name of ship may be given but place must not be mentioned.
$10^1/_4$ x $14^1/_4$in.

M1.1902. *Pencil and crayon sketch*. Port view of destroyer painted in camouflage colours. Inscribed '*Obdurate*, foredeck and silhouette before refit 1944. Allanson Hick'.
Built by Denny and launched in March 1941 *Obdurate* bore the pendant number G39. She helped protect convoy JW56A, comprising twenty ships, the first Arctic convoy to sail after the sinking of the *Scharnhorst*. They left Loch Ewe on 12 January 1944 and were pursued by a force of ten U-boats. Three merchantmen were lost and *Obdurate* was damaged by an aerial acoustic torpedo. Like all the O class she survived the hostilities; she remained in the Royal Navy and was eventually scrapped at Inverkeithing in 1964.
Censor's stamp on reverse 'Not to be published'. $8^3/_4$ x $9^3/_4$in.

(32) M1.1903. *Pencil drawing*. Bow port side view of destroyer in dry dock. Barrage balloons in distance. Inscribed 'Tues. Aug. 11, 1942. 2.30-4.30pm 12th, 9am-11am. *Faulknor's* refit 1942. Study in dry dock'. Signed in right hand corner Allanson . . . (remainder cut off).
HMS *Faulknor* a destroyer of the F (*Fearless*) class was built by Yarrow and launched 12 June 1934. As part of the Home Fleet based at Scapa Flow she was very quickly into action when on 14 September 1939 in company with *Foxhound* and *Firedrake* she depth charged U39. Forced to surface the crew were made prisoners and less than a week later U27 was added to the tally. At Narvik in April 1940 she attacked German supply ships and bombarded gun emplacements on the

short and with *Zulu* came under intensive aerial attack in Ofotfjord but suffered no hits. On 17 April the two vessels attacked a German destroyer and set her on fire before attacking the shore installations. Suffering damage to her Asdic dome *Faulkner* put into Grimsby for repairs before joining Force H in the Mediterranean, in June the same year. For a time she was attached to Force M based at Freetown, Sierra Leone, in support of various Free French sections against Vichy forces at Dakar and in the French Cameroons. In the Mediterranean again the starboard engine failed and *Faulkner* sailed to Portsmouth for a three month long refit before rejoining the Home Fleet at Scapa Flow in November 1941, making regular sorties into the North Atlantic on the alert for the *Tirpitz* which posed an ever present threat to the northern convoys.

She formed part of the cover for convoys PQ9 and PQ10 from Iceland to the Kola inlet. After supporting PQ12 *Faulknor* joined the 8th Flotilla in the abortive pursuit of *Tirpitz* off the Norway coast. After more convoy duty and exercises with the fleet, she entered Hull docks for a major refit in June 1942. The after bank of torpedo tubes removed in 1940 were put back and a 3in. HA gun replaced the X gun and two 20mm Oerlikon cannons replaced the .5in. machine guns. An improved, High Frequency Direction Finder, popularly known as the 'Huff Duff' was installed enabling radio frequencies of the U-boat to be picked up. A General Warning radar and HA Director were also fitted at the same time and she was repainted in the new 'Peter Scott' camouflage before rejoining the fleet on 28 August. She formed part of the battle squadron, heavily armed with torpedoes, assembled to protect convoy PQ18. Split into two *Faulknor* belonged to B force under the direction of HMS *Milne* and on 12 September engaged and destroyed U589. She helped escort QP15 and helped thwart the attempt by the *Lutzow* and *Hipper*, with a destroyer escort, to disrupt supplies to Russia at a time when the German army was under severe pressure on its eastern front. In her last Russian convoy RA53, homeward bound the gyro-steering gear was put out of action and *Faulknor* returned to Hull for another refit before sailing in April 1943 to Scapa Flow for convoy duty in the North Atlantic, where she was leader of the 4th Escort Group. She then joined Force H in the Mediterranean in the build up to the invasion of Sicily and assisted at the landings on the Aegean islands of Kos, Leros and Samos which after an initial success had to be evacuated owing to superior German air power. By March 1944 *Faulknor* had sailed a total of 250,000 miles and her crew received leave at Scapa before sailing to the channel as part of the invasion force. Employed as an escort for the advanced minesweeping flotilla she also joined in the heavy naval barrage of the Normandy coast. After returning to Portsmouth for fresh ammunition General Montgomery and his staff came on board and were duly landed in France to set up their headquarters. After again damaging the Asdic dome she sailed to Grimsby for repairs in July and the following month was part of the 8th Flotilla escorting coastal convoys around the south west coast. In April 1945 she was blockading German forces in the Biscay ports but was put in reserve in July that year and scrapped at Milford Haven in 1945.

Inscribed on the reverse 'not to be published'.
For a detailed account of the career of HMS *Faulknor* see Peter C. Smith *Destroyer Leader*, London, 1976.

12³/₄ x 17in.

(33) M1.1904. *Pencil and crayon drawing.* Sketch from floor of dry dock of stern of destroyer. Inscribed '*Faulknor's* refit August 14, Wm. Wright dock 1942 2pm-4.30pm. Allanson Hick'. Colour instructions bottom right.
On reverse 'Admiralty request publication to be stopped'. 12³/₄ x 17in.

(34) M1.1905. *Watercolour.* Inscribed '*Faulknor* August 5th 1942. Wm. Wright dock, Hull'. On the reverse a pen and wash drawing of a warship at anchor. 13 x 17in.

*Tugs **Rifleman** and **Pinky** of the United Towing Co. (Cat. 41).*

Destroyer in Hull docks (Cat. 20).

*Destroyer **Onslaught** (Cat. 18).*

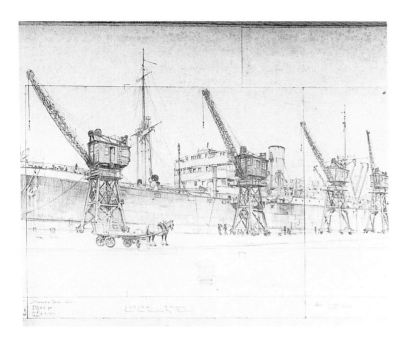

*The **Loriga,** Pacific Steam Navigation Co., Alexandra dock, 1934 (Cat. 70).*

*HMT **Tamarisk** formerly the **St. Gatien** of Thomas Hamling and Co. of Hull, 1939 (Cat. 72).*

(35) M1.1906. *Crayon and wash*. Looking forwards towards the funnels. Inscribed *'Faulknor's* refit 1942. Sketch on after deck, in dry dock. Allanson Hick'.   13 x 16in.

(36) M1.1907. *Pencil and wash*. After funnel and amidships gun. Inscribed 'Study for *Faulknor's* refit 1942 in graving dock. After funnel. Allanson Hick'. $12^1/_2$ x 16in.

(37) M1.1908. *Pen and wash*. Inscribed 'Destroyer (?) and American patrol coastal vessel. Wm. Wright dock, Hull 1942' Signed 'Allanson Hick'. On reverse a note as follows: 'Sketch to be amended as indicated, caption reads wrongly, the American patrol vessel is probably an ex-American cutter'. $12^1/_2$ x 17in.

(38) M1.1909. *Pen and wash* Amidships showing funnels. Inscribed *'Destroyer Icarus,* refit, beside crane, 1941, Allanson Hick'.
HMS *Icarus,* DO3, was built by John Brown on the Clyde and launched in November 1936. Early in 1940 she formed part of a minelaying destroyer flotilla and was then redirected to anti-submarine duties. At Narvik she captured the German transport vessel *Alster* and early in the campaign the enemy's ammunition reserves were also destroyed but unfortunately there was no military force available to follow up this advantage. *Icarus* was involved in the evacuation at Dunkirk and was part of the 4th Escort group in the Atlantic, March-May 1943, when the depredations of the U-boat wolf packs were at their height. She survived the war and was broken up in 1946.
Inscribed on reverse 'Passed for publication'.
                                    $11^1/_4$ x $13^1/_2$in.

(39) M1.1910. *Watercolour sketch* (squared up). Tugs *Rifleman* and *Pinky* in dry dock; river Hull, old High Street.
The steam tug *Pinky* was built in 1916 by Livingstone and Cooper, Hessle, for the Premier Tug Company of Hull. Sold in 1921 to the newly formed United Towing Co. she was finally broken up in 1964.
The *Rifleman* was built by Cochranes of Selby in 1945 for the Ministry of War Transport. Originally named *Empire Vera* she joined the United Towing fleet in 1947 and was scrapped in 1967.
                                    13 x $16^1/_2$in.

(40) M1.1911. *Watercolour sketch*. As the preceding (M1.1910) but more finished. $14^1/_2$ x 18in.

(41) M1.1912. *Watercolour*. Finished watercolour of *Rifleman* and *Pinky* in dry dock. Same view as M1.1910 and M1.1911. Signed Allanson Hick. $13^1/_4$ x 12in.

(42) M1.1913. *Watercolour*. Laid down on board. Port profile view of *Parma* in dock.
The four-masted steel bark was built in 1902 by A. Rogers and Co. of Port Glasgow for Anglo-American Oil. Originally named the *Arrow* she measured 3084 tons gross with an overall length of 328ft. Purchased in 1912 by F. Laeisz of Hamburg she joined the fleet as one of the famous 'flying P's'. In 1931 she was sold to a consortium which included the maritime author Alan Villiers and sailed out of Mariehamn in Finland. $13^1/_2$ x $15^1/_2$in.

M1.1914. *Ink tracing* (squared up). King George dock, Hull and the Roll on - Roll off terminal. Study for Oughtred and Harrison calendar, 1970.
                                    $16^1/_2$ x 22in.

M1.1915. *Pencil tracing*. Inscribed 'Epic of Malta p.73 (+ Tribal destroyer); starboard profile of merchantman.   6 x $10^1/_2$in.

M1.1916. *Pen and pencil tracing* (squared up). Bow starboard side view of stern trawler, H553 (?).
                                    10 x 14in.

*HMS **Inkpen** built at Beverley 1941, survived the war to become **Stella Capella**, Charleson Smith trawlers (Cat. 4).*

***Quest**, 1944, then in use as a water carrier. Built in 1917 and used by Sir Ernest Shackleton for his 1920-1 expedition (Cat. 8).*

M1.1917. *Pencil* (squared up). Starboard profile of a destroyer. $6^{1}/_{4}$ x 13in.

M1.1918. *Pencil tracing.* Portion of a destroyer. $8^{1}/_{4}$ x 11in.

M1.1919. *Pencil sketch.* Warship with tugs. $9^{3}/_{4}$ x 12in.

M1.192. *Watercolour sketch.* Oiler alongside trawler in dock. 10 x $12^{3}/_{4}$in.

(43) M1.1921. *Watercolour.* Tug; starboard view of warship. Signed Allanson Hick. $7^{1}/_{2}$ x $12^{1}/_{2}$in.

M1.1922. *Wash drawing.* Warship with three funnels. $7^{1}/_{2}$ x $12^{1}/_{2}$in.

M1.1923. *Pencil sketch.* Starboard profile of destroyer. 12 x 17in.

M1.1924. *Pencil tracing* (squared up). Bow, port side view. Inscribed '*Birmingham* sold in SMA Exhibition'. 15 x 20in.

M1.1925. *Pencil tracing.* Port view of three funnel warship. 9 x 13in.

M1.1926. *Pencil tracing.* Inscribed 'Typical V or W class destroyer, Frontispiece. Photograph HMS *Wideawake* Lt. Com. George Stitt RN'. $6^{3}/_{4}$ x $9^{1}/_{2}$in.

M1.1927. *Pen tracing.* Merchantman at dock side. $11^{1}/_{2}$ x $13^{1}/_{4}$in.

M1.1928. *Pencil tracing* (squared up). Bow, port side view of battleship. $11^{1}/_{2}$ x $16^{1}/_{2}$in.

M1.1929. *Pencil tracing.* Starboard profile of warship in Valetta (?) harbour. $12^{1}/_{2}$ x 20in.

M1.1930. *Pencil tracing* (squared up). Stern, port side view of warship (numbered 714). 11 x $15^{1}/_{2}$in.

M1.1931. *Pencil tracing* (squared up). Warships in dock. $23^{1}/_{2}$ x $33^{1}/_{4}$in.

(44) M1.1932. *Watercolour.* Bow section of warship in dock. Black band around funnel with red outline, crew on deck. Signed Allanson Hick. 14 x 19in.

(45) M1.1933. *Crayon and wash.* New Theatre, Hull. Study for calendar. 16 x $21^{1}/_{2}$in.

M1.1934. *Watercolour.* St. Mary's Church, Beverley. 21 x $25^{1}/_{2}$in.

(46) M1.1935. *Pencil and wash* (on card). Trinity House Lane; elevation, with pediment, of Hull Trinity House. 10 x 12in.

M1.1936. *Crayon and wash.* Looking forward to funnels, port side. Inscribed '*Faulknor's* refit 1942 sketch on after deck. Allanson Hick.'
Stamped on reverse 'No Admiralty objection'. 13 x 16in.

M1.1937. *Pencil and wash.* Rough sketch of country church. 10 x $13^{1}/_{2}$in.

M1.1940 - 1944: Purchased November 1990.

(47) M1.1940. *Pen drawing.* Study for calendar, inscribed 'The Hull and New Holland Ferry Boat arriving at the Corporation Pier with the compliments of Richards, Hibbert and Company'. Signed in upper margin Allanson Hick. 13 x 18in.

(48) M1.1941. *Pen drawing.* Study for calendar, inscribed 'City Hall, Hull. With best wishes for 1961 from Richards, Hibbert and Co.' Signed in bottom left corner, Allanson Hick. 15 x 14in.

(49) M1.1942. *Pen drawing*. Study for calendar, inscribed 'Guildhall, Kingston upon Hull with best wishes for 1962 from Richards, Hibbert and company'. Signed bottom right corner Allanson Hick.

15 x 17in.

(50) M1.1943. *Pen drawing*. Study for calendar, inscribed 'With best wishes for 1969 from Richards, Hibbert and Company. The New Theatre, Kingston Square, formerly known as the Assembly Rooms was designed in 1830 by Charles Mountain Hull's leading Georgian architect.' Signed bottom left corner Allanson Hick.

$14^1/_2$ x $18^1/_2$in.

(51) M1.1944. *Crayon or pastel and wash*. Study for calendar inscribed 'The Hull Dock Company Offices designed in 1867. Fortunately to be retained at the City's Maritime Museum. With best wishes for 1973 from Oughtred and Harrison (Insurance) Ltd. Incorporating Richard, Hibbert and Company'. Signed bottom right corner Allanson Hick.

13 x 17in.

(52) M1.1949. *Litho*. The bark *Pamir*. Marked 'Litho' in bottom left hand corner and the artist's signature on the right with date, 1937.

The four masted bark *Pamir* was built by Blohm and Voss in 1905 for F. Laeisz, Hamburg, as one of the famous fleet of 'flying P's'. In 1931 sold to Gustaf Erikson, Mariehamn for £4000. Taken as a prize in New Zealand in 1941 and returned to Erikson's 1948. Sold for scrap two years later but was turned into a training ship. She was lost in a hurricane in mid-Atlantic, 21 September 1957, returning to Germany from Buenos Aires with a cargo of grain. Only six of the crew of 51 cadets and 35 seamen were rescued.

16 x 21in.

Hills class trawler **Inkpen,** *1942 (Cat. 4).*

*Isles class trawler HMS **Killegray** in Princes dock, when newly commissioned, November 1941 (Cat. 3).*

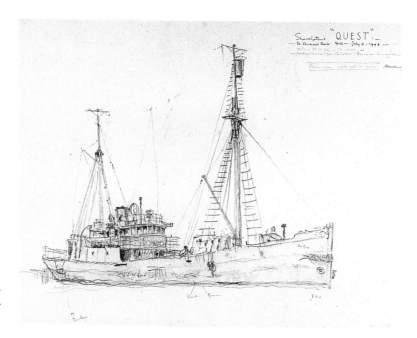

*Shackleton's **Quest,** in 1944, when used as water carrier for the corvettes based at Immingham (Cat. 8).*

Montano, *a converted trawler, and* *Garola* *fitted with acoustic hammers on their bows for mine counter-measures (Cat. 9).*

Destroyer refitting in Hull docks (Cat. 19).

*Destroyer **Onslaught** in dry dock at Hull (Cat. 22).*

(53) W.84. *Pencil and wash.* Trawlers fitting out. Signed Allanson Hick 1937. Purchased in 1938, it is a view from the upper rear window of Monument Buildings. Study for 1938 Richard, Hibbert and Co.'s calendar. $19^1/_4$ x 14in.

(54) W.534. *Pencil drawing.* Monument Buildings. Signed Allanson Hick 1935. Erected 1907-10 to the design of William Bell for the North Eastern Railway and occupied by J. Richards and Son and Co., Insurance Brokers. From 1933 styled Richards, Hibbert and Co. which became part of the Oughtred and Harrison insurance group in 1963. This drawing is a study for the first of the regular series of calendars which Hick did for Richards, Hibbert & Co. Purchased 1988 from New English Art Galleries (Hull). 17 x 20in.

(55) W.537. *Pencil and ink.* Victoria Pier from the 'Horsewash'. Signed 'Allanson Hick, Hull November 1953'. Presented by A. G. Chamberlain, 1988.
9 x $11^5/_8$in.

(56) W.538. *Watercolour.* Albion Street Congregational Church. Signed and dated 1937. The church was built 1841-2 to the design of H.F. Lockwood; it was destroyed by bombing in 1941. Presented by A. G. Chamberlain, 1988. $12^1/_2$ x $17^1/_2$in.

(57) W.539. *Pencil* (squared up). Queen Victoria Statue, City Square, looking towards Wilberforce column, in original position near Monument Bridge. Presented by A. G. Chamberlain, 1988.
$9^3/_4$ x $12^1/_4$in.

(58) W.540. *Ink and wash on paper.* Signed lower centre Allanson Hick, and inscribed lower right 'King George Dock Hull and the Continental Car Ferry with best wishes for 1970 from Oughtred and Harrison (Insurance) Ltd. Incorporating Richards, Hibbert and Company. Purchased from New English Art Galleries (Hull), 1988. 15 x 21in.
An example of the calendar derived from this drawing is also preserved in the collections of the Ferens Art Gallery; presented 1988 by A. G. Chamberlain.

(59) W.693. *Oils.* Portrait of E. H. Earle; signed 'Ernest Hall Earle, Etatis 80 1943, Allanson Hick'.
The subject was a member of the Hull Literary Club for over fifty years and was also a painter, stainer of glass, illuminator of manuscripts, actor, producer, etc. A presentation of the portrait was made to Earle at the Imperial Hotel on the occasion of his birthday (see *Hull Daily Mail),* 13 May 1943. He died, aged 87, in 1951, at 168, Victoria Avenue.
The picture was presented to the Ferens Art Gallery by the trustees of the Hull Subscription Library.
$26^1/_2$ x $22^1/_2$in.

*On the bridge of **Onslaught**
during trials, November 1944
(Cat. 23).*

*Doctor in the wardroom of
Onslaught, November 1944
(Cat. 25).*

ONSLOW
G.17

OFFA
G.29

ONSLAUGHT
G.04.

*Destroyers **Onslow**, **Offa** and **Onslaught** (Cat. 30).*

*Tribal class destroyer **Bedouin** in William Wright dock, Hull, May 1942 (Cat. 31).*

*Destroyer **Faulknor** in dry dock at Hull, August 1942 (Cat. 32).*

– National Maritime Museum –

(60) *Pen and wash 'Onslaught's new* shaft'. The artist's diploma piece for the RSMA. Royal Society of Marine Artists (diploma collection held at the National Maritime Museum, Greenwich).   (15$^1/_2$ x 19$^1/_2$in.).

(61) *Watercolour*, 'Tug's eye view'. A Blue Star cargo liner with tug *Irishman*.   (14$^3/_8$ x 19$^7/_8$in.).

– Private Collection –

(62) *Pencil sketch;* Inscribed in the upper right hand corner 'Oct. 12, 1955, 1-2pm St. Lawrence Jewry rebuilding.   (10$^3/_4$ x 14$^3/_4$in.).

(63) *Pencil sketch*. Inscribed in bottom left corner 'Poop Starboard quarter "Viking" Alexandra Dock 1936 July 1st'.   (7$^1/_2$ x 11$^1/_2$in.).

(64) *Pencil sketch* (on mill board). A view looking aft on deck of four-masted bark. Inscribed bottom left '*Parma* in Hull June 10 1933'.   (10$^1/_2$ x 14$^1/_2$in.).

(65) *Pencil sketch*. A drawing made afloat, giving a bow view of four-masted bark. Inscribed bottom left '*Passat* in tow at Spurn, Wed. July 20th 1938 from tug *Seaman*. Allanson Hick.   (15 x 11in.).

(66) *Pencil sketch*. A drawing made afloat, looking forward on deck of tug. Inscribed bottom left 'From after deck Tug *Seaman*, towing the *Passat* to sea. Wed. July 20th 1938. Allanson Hick'.   (15 x 11in.).

(67) *Pencil sketch*. Starboard profile view of four-masted bark under sail. Inscribed bottom left '*Olivebank* Alexandra Dock, Extn. Hull June 23rd and . . . 1933.   (13 x 20in.).

(68) *Pencil sketch.* Three small sheets laid down on board, squared up. Port side view of four-masted bark *Viking* with tug *Irishman* alongside. This is a study for the watercolour (Cat. 74).
Built in 1907 by Burmeister and Wain, Copenhagen, as a training ship for merchant officers in Denmark. Sold in 1915 to the Associated Steamship Co. and then in July 1929 to Gustaf Erikson of Mariehamn to be used in the Australian grain trade. Sold in 1950 to Gothenburg to be used as a Marine School.   (16 x 22in.).

(69) *Watercolour*. Paper laid down on board. View of bow and starboard side of four-masted bark *Passat* signed Allanson Hick 1938. A label on the reverse inscribed '*Passat* towed to sea, barque *Passat* under bare poles towed from the Humber, June 1938 Allanson Hick F.R.I.B.A., 4 Bond Street, Hull'.

(70) *Pencil sketch*. Five small sheets laid down on board. Port side view of merchantman at dock-side. Inscribed bottom left 'Alexandra Dock, Hull 16.30-1810, 3.5.1934; 17.15-19.45, 4.5.1934', centre, '*Loriga*, Glasgow, Pacific Steam Navigation Coy, Twin screw' right, 'Also 16.45-19.15, 7.5.1934'.   (13 x 22in.).

(71) *Pen and wash*. View of trawler fitting out in Princes Dock as seen from Monument Buildings.   (11 x 15in.).

(72) *Pencil and wash*. Port side view of armed trawler. Inscribed bottom right HMT *Tamarisk*. Converted trawler (Hull) Princes Dock by Amos and Smith. Tues. May 9th 1939* Interview [with] C.I.D. Inspector as result of my sketching this'.
Built as the *St. Gatien* by Cook Welton and Gemmell, Beverley, in 1925 for T. Hamling and Co. of Hull. Purchased for the Royal Navy in 1939 and sunk by German aircraft in the Thames estuary 12.8.1940.   (9$^1/_2$ x 11in.).

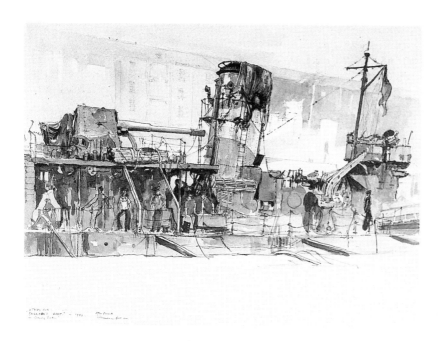

Faulknor in William Wright dock, August 1942 (Cat. 33).

Study for **Faulknor's** refit, 1942 (Cat. 36).

(73) *Watercolour.* The four-masted bark *Pommern* signed and dated 1935. Exhibited at the Royal Academy. (15 x 20in.).

(74) *Watercolour.* The four-masted bark *Viking* with tug *Irishman* alongside. Signed Allanson Hick (15 x 20in.).

(75) *Watercolour.* Stern, port side view of motor vessel with lighters alongside in the Hull docks. (9 x 12in.).

(76) *Watercolour.* Theatre Royal, Haymarket with bus, taxi and roadmenders in view. ($13^1/_4$ x 17in.).

(77) *Pencil drawing.* Study for the preceding. Inscribed '12.30 June 14th and forenoon June 16 1930. First night of Ivor Novello's 'Comedienne'. Allanson Hick, Theatre Royal, Haymarket'. (9 x 12in.).

(78) *Pastel.* Full rigged ship, port side view. (14 x $15^3/_4$in,).

(79) *Pencil drawing.* Inscribed 'SEAPRO Alexandra Dock Extn. Hull June 14 and 20 1933. This ship was originally fitted up to fish in foreign waters by means of the launches carried on board and to can the fish immediately in her own self-contained factory, by Messrs. Sea Products Ltd. about 1927 or 1928. The enterprise however went bankrupt and this ship never put to sea, but laid up in Hull until towed away on Monday October 2nd to be broken up 1933'. 'Allanson Hick 1933 study for watercolour entitled 'Dockland' sold in Royal Academy Exhibition 1935'. ($9^3/_4$ x 12in.).

(80) *Pencil drawing.* Inscribed 'TUGS and TENDERS Minerva Pier, Hull. Study for aquatint 15.50-17.05, 2.5.1934' Signed Allanson Hick. (9 x $11^1/_2$in.).

(81) *Oil.* Unfinished study of Lincoln Cathedral from Brayford Pool; intended for a British Rail poster design. (18 x 26in.).

(82) *Watercolour.* Dunfermline Abbey, October 1964. ($19^1/_2$ x $7^1/_2$in.).

(83) *Watercolour.* Guildhall, Stirling Castle. (11 x $14^3/_4$in.).

(84) *Watercolour.* St. Paul's Cathedral surrounded by post-war reconstruction. (10 x 20in.).

(85) *Watercolour.* Carlton House Terrace. ($11^1/_2$ x $15^1/_2$in.).

(86) *Watercolour.* St. Mary Lowgate, Hull. (18 x 26in).

(87) *Watercolour.* Antiquaries at Newbald, 1967. (Field trip of East Riding Antiquarian Society). ($9^3/_4$ x $13^1/_2$in.).

(88) *Watercolour.* Stern port side view of merchantman; coal gantry and United Towing tug in Hull docks. ($17^1/_4$ x 14in.).

(89) *Pencil and wash.* Scaffolding surrounding York Minster, 1957. (18 x 14in.).

(90) *Oil.* Blue star vessel, *Imperial Star,* port side view. ($21^3/_4$ x $29^3/_4$in.).

(91) *Watercolour.* Kilchrenan, Lock Awe, 19 April 1969. ($10^1/_2$ x $14^1/_2$in.).

(92) *Watercolour.* Elcho Castle, Perthshire. (12 x $8^3/_4$in.).

(93) *Poster.* 'The Continent via Hull and Goole'. Printed for British Railways Eastern Region in the 1950s by Jordison and Co. Ltd. in double royal size; it advertises the services of Associated Humber Lines which were linked to the rail network.   (25 x 40in.).

– Messrs. Gelder & Kitchen –

(94) *Oil.* The ss *Clan Sutherland* in King George Dock.   (19$^1/_2$ x 23in.).

– Private Collection –

(95) *Watercolour.* Forth railway bridge; 1932.
(24 x 30in.).

(96) *Watercolour.* Tay bridge – the Tay at Perth; 1936.
(21 x 24$^1/_2$in.).

(97) *Watercolour.* Bow view of four-masted bark (port side).   (22 x 25in.).

(98) *Watercolour.* St. Mary's church, Beverley; riders in foreground.   (23 x 26in.).

(99) *Pencil drawing.* Bow view of *Parma.*
(15$^1/_4$ x 12$^1/_2$in.).

Section of Mulberry harbour used as a temporary replacement for the Riverside Quay, sketched in 1947 (Cat. 2).

Trawlers on slip at St. Andrew's dock, Hull.

New Theatre, Hull, study for calendar (Cat. 45).

Tattershall Castle and Corporation Pier,
study for calendar (Cat. 47).

The Hull and New Holland Ferryboat
arriving at the Corporation Pier
with the Compliments of
· Richards, Hibbert & Company ·

THE OFFICES *of* MESSRS. RICHARDS, HIBBERT & C?   ALLANSON HICK · 1935.

Monument Buildings, 1935 (Cat. 54).

Oil portrait of E. H. Earle, 1943 (Cat. 59).

*Pen and wash version of **'Onslaught's** new shaft' presented as the artist's diploma piece to the RSMA (Cat. 60, National Maritime Museum).*

'Tug's eye view' (Cat. 61, National Maritime Museum).

APPENDIX 1

Allanson Hick (1898-1975): elected to Society of Graphic Artists 1936, founder member of the Royal Society of Marine Artists, Fellow of the Royal Institute of British Architects, member of the Art Workers' Guild. He exhibited at the Salom de la Marine, Paris, 1946, at the Royal Scottish Academy and the Royal Academy, London, 1935-1955.

His subjects hung at the R.A. are as follows:

1935	799	Ballast for Mariehamn (this was the *Pommern).*
	821	Dockland.
	831	Bunkers.
1940	745	Dory depots.
	777	Seven for tomorrow.
1943	672	High Water.
1944	989	Tired destroyer – pencil (probably one of the O class destroyers drawn while refitting in Hull Docks).
1945	976	Albert Dock, Hull.
	982	Destroyer refit.
1948	1034	*Onslaught* new shaft – pencil and wash (O class destroyer refitting in Hull Docks in 1944).
1949	976	Dockside oiler.
1954	795	All Souls, Langham Place.
1955	834	Theatre Royal, Haymarket.
	888	Rebuilding the city.

St. Lawrence Jewry, London, rebuilding after the war, 1955 (Cat. 62).

St. Mary's Lowgate, Hull (Cat. 86).

APPENDIX 2

Calendar subject exhibited in 1976.

1. The New Offices, 1933
   Pencil drawing; $11^1/_4$ x $8^7/^8$in.

2. Queen Victoria Square, 1934
   Crayon and wash; $14^1/_4$ x $21^7/_8$in.

3. Monument Buildings
   Crayon and wash.

4. Paragon Street
   Ink and wash; $12^1/_2$ x 16in.

5. Drypool Bridge
   Crayon, ink and wash; 13 x $18^1/_4$in.

6. The Hull and New Holland Ferry
   Ink; $12^3/_4$ x 18in.

7. The Market Cross at Beverley
   Ink; $10^1/_2$ x 14in.

8. City Hall, Hull, 1961
   Ink; 15 x $13^3/_4$in.

9. Guildhall, 1962
   Ink; $13^3/_4$ x $16^3/_4$in.

10. Beverley Minster, 1963
    Ink; $20^3/_4$ x $16^3/_4$in. (this was the year in which Richards, Hibbert were absorbed within the Oughtred and Harrison group).

11. St. Mary's, Beverley, 1964
    Ink; $17^7/_8$ x $24^1/_2$in.

12. Patrington Church, 1965
    Ink; $16^3/_8$ x $14^1/_2$in.

13. St. Mary's Lowgate, Hull, 1966
    Ink; $16^5/_8$ x $19^7/_8$in.

14. The North Bar, Beverley
    Ink; 17 x $14^3/_4$in.

15. The New Theatre, Kingston Square, 1969
    Ink; $13^7/_8$ x 18in.

16. King George Dock and the Continental Car Ferry, 1970
    Ink and wash; $14^7/_8$ x 21in.

17. The Lord Mayor's Parlour, Guildhall, Hull, 1971
    Ink and wash; $17^1/_4$ x $14^1/_2$in.

18. Royal Station Hotel, 1972
    Ink; $18^1/_2$ x 21in.

19. Hull Dock Company Offices, 1973
    Crayon and wash; $13^7/_8$ x $16^3/_4$in.

20. Central Library, 1974
    Pencil and wash; $19^3/_4$ x $15^3/_4$in.

Scaffolding — at · York · 1957 · Allanson Hick

Scaffolding surrounding York Minster (Cat. 89).

*Ballast for Mariehamn, **Pommern** (Royal Academy 1935).*

Associated Humber Line poster (Cat. 93).